About the Author

A mother, social worker and daughter of African parents, Geraldine Moyo recognised that children want to talk about their colour. They want to talk about their history and that of their friends. Geraldine cleverly and simplistically brings together these issues in a fun, educational and age appropriate way. Apart from the adventure *My Africa* takes a child and parent through at bedtime, this book is also an instrument for teachers and social care practitioners to talk about their Africa.

My Africa

Geraldine Moyo

My Africa

Olympia Publishers
London

www.olympiapublishers.com
OLYMPIA PAPERBACK EDITION

A CIP catalogue record for this title is
available from the British Library.

ISBN: 978-1-78830-345-3

This is a work of fiction.
Names, characters, places and incidents originate from the writer's
imagination. Any resemblance to actual persons, living or dead, is
purely coincidental.

First Published in 2021

Olympia Publishers
Tallis House
2 Tallis Street
London
EC4Y 0AB

Printed in Great Britain

Dedication

To my Reasons for being, Alexander Thando Ifiok Umoh and Anthony Mandla Etido Umoh. I loved you before you were and now even more so.

In a place far away where you use a boat or a plane to get there.

Is the big continent of Africa with many countries such as Nigeria, Sierra Leone and Kenya.

Can you think of another African country?

While hyenas and cheetahs play in the glare
of the sun.

Ostriches, wildebeest and zebras walk around the savanna looking for some leaves and grass.

Can you find your favourite African animal?

In Africa there are different kinds of lovely
foods such as
sweet plantains,
nutty domoda
and yummy puff- puffs.

What African foods you have tried?

Some of the foods are tastier to eat using
your hands such as injera made with the
ancient grain teff, amatshakada made from
kernels of maize and gari made from the
bitter sweet root called cassava.

Can you think of a food you love to eat with
your hands?

Timbuktu was built by the Tuareg.
South Africans sing and dance artistically,
Ghanaians make beautiful printed patterns,
Ivorians are skilful at kicking the ball,
the Senegalese play the djembe with great might.

Can you think of other things
Africans are good at?

Doctor

Pilot

Police Officer

Tennis Player

Fire Fighter

Ballet Dancer

Footballer

Musician

OUR L

Many Africans who live on continents such as
Europe and the Americas came on a boat or a
plane from far away Africa.

WORLD

Some Africans are a beautiful black colour, some a beautiful yellow, some a beautiful white, some a beautiful brown.

OUR AFRI

Whatever their colour they celebrate the amazing continent of Africa where they came from.